THE ULTIMATE
CLEVELAND BROWNS
TRIVIA BOOK

A Collection of Amazing Trivia Quizzes and Fun Facts for Die-Hard Browns Fans!

Ray Walker

Exclusive Free Book

Crazy Sports Stories

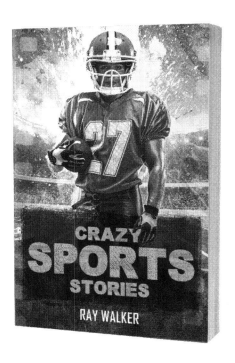

As a thank you for getting a copy of this book I would like to offer you a free copy of my book Crazy Sports Stories which comes packed with interesting stories from your favorite sports such as Football, Hockey, Baseball, Basketball and more.

Grab your free copy over at

RayWalkerMedia.com/Bonus

CONTENTS

INTRODUCTION

Team fandom should be inspirational. Our attachment to our favorite teams should fill us with pride, excitement, loyalty, and a sense of fulfillment in knowing that we are part of a community with many other fans who feel the same way.

Browns fans are no exception. With a rich, successful history in the NFL, the Browns have inspired their supporters to strive for greatness with their tradition of colorful players, memorable eras, big moves, and unique moments.

This book is meant to be a celebration of those moments and an examination of the collection of interesting, impressive, or important details that allow us to understand the full stories behind the players and the team.

You may use the book as you wish. Each chapter contains 20 quiz questions in a mixture of multiple-choice and true-false formats, an answer key (Don't worry, it's on a separate page!), and a section of 10 "Did You Know?" facts about the team.

Some will use it to test themselves with the quiz questions. How much Browns history do you really know? How many of the finer points can you remember? Some will use it competitively (Isn't that the heart of sports?), waging contests with friends and fellow devotees to see who can lay claim to being the biggest fan. Some will enjoy it as a learning experience, gaining insight to enrich their fandom and add color to their understanding of their favorite team. Still others may use it to teach, sharing the wonderful anecdotes inside to inspire a new generation of fans to hop aboard the Browns bandwagon.

Whatever your purpose may be, we hope you enjoy delving into the amazing background of Browns football!

Oh…for the record, information and statistics in this book are current up to the beginning of 2021. The Browns will surely topple more records and win more awards as the seasons pass, so keep this in mind when you're watching the next game with your friends, and someone starts a conversation with "Did you know…" to share some trivia.

CHAPTER 1:

ORIGINS & HISTORY

QUIZ TIME!

1. In which year did the Browns begin playing and in which league were they originally a franchise?

    a. 1928, in the North Eastern Football Association
    b. 1946, in the All-America Football Conference
    c. 1950, in the National Football League
    d. 1961, in the American Football League

2. The franchise was nearly called the Cleveland Spiders, partially to capitalize on the popularity of the Spider-Man comics at the time and partially to honor a defunct baseball team from the city by that name.

    a. True
    b. False

3. How was the nickname "Browns" chosen for the team?

    a. It was decided that the team would have no logo, so the franchise was named after the color of its uniforms.

b. It was selected by the team's original ownership, a group of three men who had all attended Brown University.

c. It was picked to provide contrast and distinguish the team from Ohio's other major sports franchise at the time, the Cincinnati Reds.

d. It was chosen to honor the founder of the team, Paul Brown.

4. In which season did the Browns begin to play in their new stadium (FirstEnergy Stadium) after moving from their longtime home at Cleveland Stadium?

   a. 1993
   b. 1999
   c. 2000
   d. 2011

5. Who was the founder of the Cleveland Browns?

   a. Paul Brown
   b. Art Modell
   c. Jimmy Haslam
   d. Otto Graham

6. In which season did the Browns earn their first playoff berth?

   a. 1946
   b. 1950
   c. 1961
   d. 1972

7. The Cleveland Browns won more games than any other NFL team during the period between 1950 and 1955.

    a. True

    b. False

8. How many times in their franchise history have the Browns won a division title?

    a. 6

    b. 9

    c. 12

    d. 17

9. Which of the following players was NOT among the group of the first Browns players ever to be named as Cleveland's representatives on the NFL All-Pro Team?

    a. Quarterback Otto Graham

    b. Fullback Marion Motley

    c. Guard Bill Willis

    d. End Mac Speedie

10. Where do the Browns rank among NFL franchises when it comes to most Super Bowl trophies won?

    a. 4th overall

    b. 17th overall

    c. 23rd overall

    d. Tied for last overall

11. How did the Browns fare during their 50th anniversary season in the NFL?

a. Missed the playoffs

b. Lost in the first round to the Denver Broncos

c. Lost in the conference championship to the Pittsburgh Steelers

d. Lost in the Super Bowl to the Dallas Cowboys

12. The longest stretch the Browns have gone without making the playoffs is 17 years, between 2003 and 2019.

a. True

b. False

13. Which team did Cleveland face in its first NFL game (which resulted in a 35-10 victory)?

a. Pittsburgh Steelers

b. Philadelphia Eagles

c. Baltimore Colts

d. New York Giants

14. What were the details surrounding the Browns' first shutout in the NFL?

a. It occurred in 1957, a 7-0 loss to the New York Giants.

b. It occurred in 1953, a 14-0 win over the Pittsburgh Steelers.

c. It occurred in 1950, a 6-0 loss to the New York Giants.

d. It occurred in 1950, a 31-0 win over the Baltimore Colts.

15. Which player kicked the team's first field goal ever?

a. Otto Graham

b. Mac Speedie

    c. Lou Groza

    d. Dante Lavelli

16. As of 2021, Cleveland is tied with the Green Bay Packers and Pittsburgh Steelers as the franchises that have sent more players to the Pro Bowl than any other NFL franchise.

    a. True

    b. False

17. How did Cleveland fare in its first NFL playoff run?

    a. Lost in the first round to the Chicago Cardinals

    b. Lost in the conference playoffs to the New York Giants

    c. Lost in the NFL Championship to the Detroit Lions

    d. Won the NFL Championship over the Los Angeles Rams

18. What is Cleveland's franchise record for most victories recorded by the club in a single regular season (in either the AAFC or the NFL)?

    a. 10

    b. 12

    c. 14

    d. 16

19. Which of the following is NOT the name of one of the official Browns mascots?

    a. Hound Dog

    b. Brownie the Elf

c. Chomps

d. Swagger

20. The Cleveland football franchise has, at some point, been included in both the Western Conference and the Eastern Conference within the NFL's division of teams.

a. True

b. False

QUIZ ANSWERS

1. B – 1946, in the All-America Football Conference

2. B – False

3. D – It was chosen to honor the founder of the team, Paul Brown.

4. B – 1999

5. A – Paul Brown

6. A – 1946

7. A – True

8. C – 12

9. A – Quarterback Otto Graham

10. D – Tied for last overall

11. A – Missed the playoffs

12. A – True

13. B – Philadelphia Eagles

14. D – It occurred in 1950, a 31-0 win over the Baltimore Colts.

15. C – Lou Groza

16. B – False

17. D – Won the NFL Championship over the Los Angeles Rams

18. C – 14

19. A – Hound Dog

20. B – False

DID YOU KNOW?

1. The very first Cleveland Browns regular-season game was a 1946 All-American Football Conference contest against the Miami Seahawks. The Browns dominated, winning 44-0 and preventing the Seahawks from ever getting beyond Cleveland's 39-yard line.

2. Cleveland had been home to three professional football teams before the Browns arrived. Both the Cleveland Bulldogs and the Cleveland Indians played in the National Football League during the 1920s and 1930s, with each wearing red and white uniforms before ceasing operations. The Cleveland Rams entered the NFL in 1937 and won the league championship in 1945, but then moved to Los Angeles.

3. FirstEnergy Stadium, the current home of the Browns, is located on the same site as the demolished Cleveland Stadium. Therefore, despite getting a brand-new stadium in 1999, the Browns have played in the same place for their entire existence, since 1946.

4. While the Browns are an anchor tenant of the FirstEnergy Stadium, it is not their home exclusively. College football, high school football, international soccer, and various concerts have been held there as well.

5. As a new team entering the NFL in 1950, the Browns arrived in a merger between the AAFC and the NFL. The

San Francisco 49ers and Baltimore Colts also came aboard at the same time, while the Los Angeles Dons merged with the Los Angeles Rams, and the Buffalo Bills, Brooklyn-New York Yankees, and Chicago Hornets all folded.

6. Cleveland's first touchdown came on a 19-yard toss from quarterback Cliff Lewis to end Mac Speedie during the first quarter of their first game, in 1946 against the Miami Seahawks.

7. Cleveland has a handful of NFL rivals, including a few important enough to have names for the rivalries. They are a part of "the Turnpike Rivalry" with the Pittsburgh Steelers, "the Battle of Ohio" with the Cincinnati Bengals, and "the Great Lakes Classic" with the Detroit Lions.

8. Cleveland's franchise record for most victories recorded by the club in a single NFL regular season is 12, which they set during the 1986 season.

9. The Cleveland Browns are one of seven NFL teams that do not have a cheerleading squad in 2021. Along with the New York Giants, they are one of just two teams that have never had an official cheerleading squad at any point during their existence.

10. In the beginning, the Cleveland Browns franchise could do no wrong. In their initial four seasons in the All-American Football Conference, the Browns won the AAFC Championship every single year. They moved to the NFL and promptly won the NFL Championship in their first season. They then proceeded to make it to the

NFL Championship game for the next five consecutive seasons, winning two more titles.

CHAPTER 2:

JERSEYS & NUMBERS

QUIZ TIME!

1. When they began playing in the NFL in 1950, the Browns used what color scheme for their home and away uniforms?

    a. Red, white, and blue

    b. Brown, green, and beige

    c. Orange, brown, and white

    d. Black, gold, and purple

2. The numbers 0 and 00 have been banned from circulation by Cleveland's ownership because they are seen to represent a losing attitude.

    a. True

    b. False

3. How many stripes run from the front of the crown to the base of the neck on the Cleveland Browns' helmets?

    a. One brown stripe

    b. Two white stripes

c. Two white stripes and one brown stripe

d. Two brown stripes and one white stripe

4. Three very good Cleveland players each wore number 33 for half a decade with the team, and each played a different position. Who were these three players?

a. Wide receiver Reggie Rucker, running back Leroy Hoard, and cornerback Daylon McCutcheon

b. Running back Earnest Byner, wide receiver Mohammed Massaquoi, and tight end David Njoku

c. Safety Donte Whitner, linebacker Galen Fiss, and running back Kevin Mack

d. Running back Peyton Hillis, wide receiver Braylon Edwards, and linebacker Dick Ambrose

5. In which year did player names first appear on the backs of Browns jerseys?

a. 1950

b. 1960

c. 1970

d. 1980

6. Which jersey has proven to be most popular with Cleveland fans in 2020, having sold the most Cleveland jerseys on NFL.com, and more jerseys than anyone in the NFL except for Kansas City Chiefs quarterback Patrick Mahomes?

a. Running back Nick Chubb's number 24 jersey

b. Wide receiver Odell Beckham Jr.'s number 13 jersey

c. Defensive end Myles Garrett's number 95 jersey

d. Quarterback Baker Mayfield's number 6 jersey

7. The Color Rush uniforms featuring brown jerseys over brown pants worn by Cleveland are often said to have been "jinxed," and therefore, the team avoids wearing them whenever the choice is theirs.

a. True

b. False

8. Who wore the unlucky jersey (number 13) for the most games in franchise history?

a. Wide receiver Odell Beckham Jr.

b. Quarterback Spergon Wynn

c. Quarterback Frank Ryan

d. Wide receiver Josh Gordon

9. The current version of the Browns uniform includes three colors: brown, white, and orange. Which of the following is the shade of orange included in their color scheme?

a. Atomic tangerine

b. Burnt orange

c. Carrot orange

d. Marmalade

10. Only one Browns player has ever worn the number 1 on his jersey. Who was this player?

a. Quarterback Tim Couch

b. Punter Tom Tupa

c. Quarterback Brady Quinn

d. Wide receiver Michael Jackson

11. Several strong running backs have worn number 34 for the Browns. Which of these players scored the most career touchdowns with Cleveland?

    a. Greg Pruitt

    b. Kevin Mack

    c. Isaiah Crowell

    d. Reuben Droughns

12. Star running back Jim Brown is the only Brown to have ever worn the number 32 on his jersey and will continue to be the only one as his number is now retired.

    a. True

    b. False

13. Why did star tight end Kellen Winslow Jr. choose to wear number 80 on the back of his jersey for Cleveland?

    a. He was born in 1980.

    b. He scored 80 touchdowns during his college career at the University of Miami.

    c. His father, Hall of Fame tight end Kellen Winslow Sr., wore number 80 during his NFL career.

    d. He wanted to honor his favorite Browns receiver, Andre Rison, who wore the number when Winslow Jr. was younger.

14. How many jersey numbers have the Cleveland Browns retired for their former players?

    a. 2

    b. 5

c. 8

d. 11

15. Which former 1ˢᵗ overall draft pick never competed for the Browns but still had his number retired by Cleveland; easily creating the shortest tenure of anyone whose number has been retired by the franchise?

   a. Quarterback Peyton Manning

   b. Quarterback Harry Gilmer

   c. Halfback Ernie Davis

   d. Defensive end Bubba Smith

16. Tackle and kicker Lou Groza wore the number 46 for more games than anyone else in Browns history. However, Groza has number 76 retired instead, and a different player has his jersey retired with number 46.

   a. True

   b. False

17. Lucky number 7 has been worn by nine Browns. Who wore it for the longest time?

   a. Punter Tom Tupa

   b. Quarterback DeShone Kizer

   c. Punter Jamie Gillan

   d. Punter Jeff Gossett

18. Who is the Browns player whose number was most recently retired by the club?

   a. Quarterback Otto Graham

   b. Running back Jim Brown

c. Punter Lou Groza

d. Defensive back Don Fleming

19. Which number did star linebacker Clay Matthews Jr., who was named to the Cleveland Browns Ring of Honor, wear?

    a. 57

    b. 55

    c. 75

    d. 60

20. The Browns have retired more jersey numbers than any other NFL franchise has.

    a. True

    b. False

QUIZ ANSWERS

1. C – Orange, brown, and white

2. B – False

3. D – Two brown stripes and one white stripe

4. A – Wide receiver Reggie Rucker, running back Leroy Hoard, and cornerback Daylon McCutcheon

5. C – 1970

6. D – Quarterback Baker Mayfield's number 6 jersey

7. B – False

8. C – Quarterback Frank Ryan

9. B – Burnt orange

10. D – Wide receiver Michael Jackson

11. A – Greg Pruitt

12. B – False

13. C – His father, Hall of Fame tight end Kellen Winslow Sr., wore number 80 during his NFL career.

14. B – 5

15. C – Halfback Ernie Davis

16. A – True

17. D – Punter Jeff Gossett

18. C – Punter Lou Groza

19. A – 57

20. B – False

DID YOU KNOW?

1. When the team started to play in the AAFC in 1946, Cleveland wore white leather helmets. They briefly wore orange leather helmets for four weeks when they moved to the NFL in 1950 but decided to keep the white motif until eventually changing to orange plastic helmets in 1952.

2. The highest number ever sported by a Brown is 99. It has been worn by over a dozen players but was probably most notably worn by defensive lineman Orpheus Roye during the 2000s.

3. Current Browns star quarterback Baker Mayfield is perhaps the most famous player on the team, but Mayfield never had the chance to choose his jersey number. When he was a walk-on in college at Texas Tech University, Mayfield was given number 6. The same thing happened when he transferred to the University of Oklahoma and when he was drafted by the Browns. Mayfield had preferred number 11, which he wore in high school.

4. Throughout most of their history, the Browns always wore white pants on the field. This changed in 1975 when the team switched to orange pants, a look that remained until 1984. Later, in 2008, Cleveland added solid brown pants to their rotation, and they are still used with the current versions of their uniforms.

5. The first time Cleveland wore any sort of patch on their uniform was in 1969. The team added an insignia on the left shoulders of their jerseys to commemorate the 50th anniversary of the NFL.

6. In 1965, the Browns hired a company named Creative Services to design a logo to be placed on their helmets. The company came up with an interlocking design featuring a "C" and a "B," but this was never used during games. The team's helmets have featured stripes throughout the years but remain logo-less to this day.

7. Superstition may have scared some Browns away from wearing the number 13. Only ten players in franchise history have chosen it for themselves. Popular wide receiver Odell Beckham Jr. claims it currently, which has made it an unusually big seller with fans of the team.

8. Since 1973, the NFL no longer allows players to wear jersey number 0 or 00. No Cleveland Brown ever wore either number in the 27 seasons before this change, so neither number will ever be used in franchise history.

9. The highest number ever retired by the Cleveland Browns is number 76, belonging to Lou "the Toe" Groza. Groza played center, offensive tackle, defensive tackle, and kicker for the team between 1946 and 1967, winning four NFL Championships while appearing in a team-record 268 games with the club.

10. For a decade, from 2003 to 2014, Cleveland uniforms included a memorial shoulder patch in honor of deceased

team owner Al Lerner. Lerner had passed away in 2002 after a battle with brain cancer.

CHAPTER 3:

CATCHY NICKNAMES

QUIZ TIME!

1. By which nickname are the Browns' fans most commonly referred to?

    a. "Dawgs"
    b. "Brownies"
    c. "Ottos"
    d. "Orange Grove"

2. Browns quarterback Johnny Manziel was often referred to as "The Bust" thanks to a double meaning; Manziel earned a literal bust as a Heisman Trophy winner in college but could not make the successful leap to the NFL and did not live up to his hype.

    a. True
    b. False

3. The longtime home of the Browns, FirstEnergy Stadium, was also more commonly known by which popular nickname?

a. "The Mistake by the Lake"

b. "The Cleveland Kennel"

c. "The Factory of Sadness"

d. "Brown Town"

4. An NFL rule that two unsportsmanlike conduct penalties within the same game is grounds for ejection from that game is unofficially named for a Cleveland Brown and known colloquially as which of the following?

a. "The Odell Beckham Jr. Rule"

b. "The Clay Matthews Jr. Rule"

c. "The Myles Garrett Rule"

d. "The Baker Mayfield Rule"

5. Why was Browns linebacker Thomas Johnson more commonly known around the league as "Pepper"?

a. Johnson was known for sneezing fits that he could not stop, even after dozens of sneezes.

b. As a child, Johnson liked to add black pepper to his breakfast cereal for extra flavor.

c. Whenever he intercepted a pass, Johnson would shake his body to avoid being tackled.

d. During meetings and practices, Johnson was always drinking Dr. Pepper instead of water or Gatorade.

6. The Cleveland Browns have a fan club called "the Browns Backers," which has over how many official members?

a. 1,000

b. 10,000

c. 100,000

d. 1,000,000

7. Cleveland punter Tom Tupa was known as "Two-Point Tupa" because he was the first kick holder to pick up the ball on an extra point attempt and run it into the end zone after the NFL legalized two-point conversions.

   a. True

   b. False

8. Browns wide receiver Josh Gordon shared a surname with the alter ego of a comic book character, earning him which of the following superhero nicknames?

   a. "Spider-Man"

   b. "Superman"

   c. "The Flash"

   d. "The Incredible Hulk"

9. What was Cleveland head coach Eric Mangini also known as?

   a. "Eric the Terrible"

   b. "Sweet Papa Brown"

   c. "The Top Dawg"

   d. "The Man-Genius"

10. Browns guard Floyd Womack went by which edible two-word nickname?

   a. "T-Bone"

   b. "Pork Chop"

   c. "Waffle House"

   d. "Gravy Train"

11. Which Browns linebacker was known to fans and teammates by the nickname "The Assassin" due to his vicious tackling on the field?

    a. Michael Dean Perry
    b. Clay Matthews Jr.
    c. Eddie Johnson
    d. D'Qwell Jackson

12. After engaging in two memorable fights with his former Cleveland teammates as a newly traded member of the Miami Dolphins, former Browns wide receiver Paul Warfield earned the nickname "The Vengeful Ex."

    a. True
    b. False

13. Which bruising Browns running back was known to teammates by the nickname "The Albino Rhino"?

    a. Peyton Hillis
    b. Jamel White
    c. Tommy Vardell
    d. Trent Richardson

14. An NFL rule enacted in 1956 and informally known as "The Lou Groza Rule," named after the longtime Cleveland kicker, prohibits which of the following actions?

    a. "Using a steel-toed shoe to increase the distance of a kick"
    b. "Feigning contact after a kick has been executed, when none has occurred"

c. "Using an artificial medium to assist in the execution of a kick"

d. "Approaching the ball on a kick attempt from a distance of further than 15 yards away"

15. At times during his tenure in Cleveland, Browns defensive end Lyle Alzado was referred to by the nickname "Three Mile Lyle." Why?

a. Every game day morning, Alzado would run three miles from his home to the stadium to burn off some anxious energy before the kickoff.

b. Alzado played to the whistle, and frequently beyond, so that instead of going the extra mile to make a tackle, he was said to be willing to go an extra three miles.

c. Alzado was prone to compounding mistakes on plays, making them worse, so a small incident could turn into something as bad as the Three Mile Island nuclear disaster.

d. Alzado had a quick temper, violent streak, and steroid-enhanced body, so three miles was considered a safe distance to be from Alzado when he got angry.

16. Cleveland quarterback Brian Hoyer was called "Father Brian" by his young teammates because he was brought in to provide leadership and playoff experience while demonstrating how to act like a professional athlete.

a. True

b. False

17. Which current Cleveland position group is known as "The Legion of Vroom" because of the speed of the players at that position?

    a. Wide receivers and tight ends
    b. Safeties and cornerbacks
    c. Running backs
    d. Linebackers

18. What occupation did the main character, Hopalong Cassidy, have in the popular Clarence Mulford books and movies that gave a nickname to Browns halfback Howard "Hopalong" Cassady?

    a. Pirate
    b. Astronaut
    c. Detective
    d. Cowboy

19. Because of their many close games and exciting play style, the 1979 and 1980 editions of the Browns became known by what nickname?

    a. "The Last-Minute Brigade"
    b. "The Don't Blink Browns"
    c. "The Kardiac Kids"
    d. "The Cleveland Nailbiters"

20. While "Butterfingers" is a popular nickname for players who can't catch well, Browns end Dante Lavelli was so sure-handed that he received an opposite type of nickname: "Gluefingers."

a. True
b. False

QUIZ ANSWERS

1. A – "Dawgs"

2. B – False

3. C – "The Factory of Sadness"

4. A – "The Odell Beckham Jr. Rule"

5. B – As a child, Johnson liked to add black pepper to his breakfast cereal for extra flavor.

6. C – 100,000

7. A – True

8. C – "The Flash"

9. D – "The Man-Genius"

10. B – "Pork Chop"

11. C – Eddie Johnson

12. B – False

13. A – Peyton Hillis

14. C – "Using an artificial medium to assist in the execution of a kick"

15. D – Alzado had a quick temper, violent streak, and steroid-enhanced body, so three miles was considered a safe distance to be from Alzado when he got angry.

16. B – False

17. A – Wide receivers and tight ends

18. D – Cowboy

19. C – "The Kardiac Kids"

20. A – True

DID YOU KNOW?

1. Team founder Arthur McBride was the first owner of the franchise and named them the "Browns" after his first head coach, Paul Brown. Brown tried to persuade McBride not to do so, and McBride chose a second name, the "Panthers," then conducted a contest to see which would win. When another businessman came forward to declare that he owned the rights to "Panthers," "Browns" was chosen, and history was made.

2. The conservative style of football employed by Browns coach Marty Schottenheimer was derided by critics as "Marty Ball." This philosophy usually involved a powerful run game, short, safe passes, and a stout defense, but it was not very exciting to watch.

3. No American colleges use the nickname "Browns," which means that, unlike most NFL teams, Cleveland has never drafted a player whose nickname did not change upon joining the NFL.

4. The backfield tandem of running backs Nick Chubb and Kareem Hunt has recently found great success for the Browns. The duo, which splits playing time fairly evenly between them, has come to be known by the abrupt, surname-combining nickname "Chunt."

5. The NFL created a new entry in its rulebook, which was unofficially known as "The Greg Pruitt Rule." Pruitt

would often wear jerseys that were cut or otherwise designed to tear off easily when defenders grabbed him to make a tackle. The league outlawed this type of attire in 1979, though Pruitt was still selected for the Pro Bowl in 1979 and 1980 with a regular uniform.

6. The popular term for sections of fans in the Browns' stadium, "the Dawg Pound," originated with Cleveland cornerback Hanford Dixon, who would frequently bark at his teammates on the field, inspiring the spectators to pick up on this and do the same.

7. The Browns once drafted a wide receiver named Elbert Dubenion, who was supremely fast but could not catch very well. He was eventually nicknamed "Golden Wheels" by a sarcastic teammate.

8. Although his time in Cleveland was not very successful, Browns coach Bill Belichick at least obeyed all the rules. Later, when Belichick became embroiled in multiple scandals during his successful tenure in New England, he became known as "Bill Belicheat."

9. Cleveland's Tyrod Taylor did not have the biggest throwing arm, but he was able to scramble and buy some time by avoiding pass rushers. This led to the quarterback being nicknamed after an American wireless phone company: "T-Mobile."

10. Browns fans know one particular play by the simple nickname "The Fumble." This occurred during the 1987 AFC Championship against the Denver Broncos with a

Super Bowl berth on the line. With just over a minute left in the game, running back Earnest Byner coughed up the ball on what appeared to be a sure game-tying touchdown run, costing the Browns the game. Byner already had 187 yards and two touchdowns, but few remember his excellent play because of the game's heartbreaking finish.

CHAPTER 4:

THE QUARTERBACKS

QUIZ TIME!

1. Which of these Browns quarterbacks was sacked the most during his career (259 times)?

   a. Brian Sipe

   b. Tim Couch

   c. Bernie Kosar

   d. Mike Phipps

2. Quarterback Bernie Kosar holds the top three spots on the Browns' all-time list of most passing touchdowns thrown in a season.

   a. True

   b. False

3. Which quarterback has thrown the most interceptions in franchise history?

   a. Derek Anderson

   b. Otto Graham

   c. Tim Couch

   d. Brian Sipe

4. Who is the Browns' all-time career leader in passing yards?

a. Brian Sipe

b. Bernie Kosar

c. Frank Ryan

d. Otto Graham

5. Who set the franchise record for most passing yards in a season by a Cleveland quarterback with 4,132 and is the only one ever to crack 4,000 yards?

a. Baker Mayfield

b. Derek Anderson

c. Bernie Kosar

d. Brian Sipe

6. How many quarterbacks who have played for the Browns have been elected to the Pro Football Hall of Fame?

a. 1: Otto Graham

b. 2: Otto Graham and Len Dawson

c. 3: Otto Graham, Len Dawson, and Brian Sipe

d. 5: Otto Graham, Len Dawson, Brian Sipe, Bernie Kosar, and Vinny Testaverde

7. Otto Graham played more games at quarterback for the Browns than anyone else.

a. True

b. False

8. One journeyman Browns quarterback has been a member of thirteen NFL teams, more than any other franchise leader. Who was this well-traveled player?

a. Brian Hoyer

b. Josh Johnson

c. Josh McCown

d. Case Keenum

9. Who was the youngest player in the team's history to start at quarterback, at just 21 years old?

a. Tim Couch

b. DeShone Kizer

c. Johnny Manziel

d. Milt Plum

10. Which Cleveland quarterback and former 1st round draft pick was released from the team to make way for rookie Johnny Manziel after the Browns took Manziel in the 2014 NFL Draft?

a. Colt McCoy

b. Brady Quinn

c. Tim Couch

d. Brandon Weeden

11. How old was Browns quarterback Josh McCown when he retired from playing in the NFL?

a. 22 years old

b. 36 years old

c. 40 years old

d. 45 years old

12. Browns quarterback Vinny Testaverde named previous quarterback Bernie Kosar as the godfather when his daughter Maria was born in 1995.

a. True

b. False

13. Which of the following NFL records is NOT held by legendary Browns quarterback Otto Graham?

   a. Highest winning percentage as a starter, 81%

   b. Most consecutive passes thrown without an interception, 372 attempts

   c. Most career yards averaged per pass attempt, 8.63 yards

   d. Highest percentage of seasons playing in the championship game, 100%

14. Browns quarterback Otto Graham became the first person ever to win championships in two of North America's major sports after playing professionally in which other sport as well as football?

   a. Basketball

   b. Hockey

   c. Baseball

   d. Golf

15. Young Browns leader DeShone Kizer holds the franchise's record for most rushing yards in a season by a quarterback, which he set in 2017. How many yards did he rack up?

   a. 206

   b. 419

   c. 758

   d. 1,033

16. Browns quarterback Vinny Testaverde has won both a College Football National Championship and an NFL Super Bowl.

    a. True
    b. False

17. For which of the following teams did quarterback Johnny Manziel NOT play in an attempt to revive his football career after becoming a bust with the Browns?

    a. Rhein Fire of NFL Europe
    b. Hamilton Tiger-Cats of the Canadian Football League
    c. The Zappers of the indoor Fan Controlled Football
    d. Memphis Express of the Alliance of American Football

18. Cleveland quarterback Brian Sipe was picked off from the Oakland Raiders 13-yard line with less than a minute to play in a 1980 playoff game in a huge moment that became widely remembered by which infamous play call?

    a. "Eagle Zipper Hero"
    b. "Blue Trips Crosser"
    c. "17 Wide Curl"
    d. "Red Right 88"

19. How many times did quarterback Otto Graham throw for 20 or more touchdowns in a season?

    a. 0
    b. 1
    c. 3
    d. 6

20. Among quarterbacks who have started at least five games with Cleveland, Tommy O'Connell has the highest interception percentage, with 7.8% of his passes being picked off.

    a. True
    b. False

QUIZ ANSWERS

1. C – Bernie Kosar

2. B – False

3. D – Brian Sipe

4. A – Brian Sipe

5. D – Brian Sipe

6. B – 2: Otto Graham and Len Dawson

7. A – True

8. B – Josh Johnson

9. B – DeShone Kizer

10. D – Brandon Weeden

11. C – 40 years old

12. B – False

13. B – Most consecutive passes thrown without an interception, 372 attempts

14. A – Basketball

15. B – 419

16. B – False

17. A – Rhein Fire of NFL Europe

18. D – "Red Right 88"

19. C – 3

20. A – True

DID YOU KNOW?

1. Two Browns quarterbacks own a share of the longest passing plays in Browns history, 99 yards. Otto Graham accounted for one in 1947, when the Browns were in the AAFC. Then, in 2004, Jeff Garcia notched one in the NFL for Cleveland. He dropped back and found talented receiver André Davis for a touchdown toss that helped the Browns defeat the Cincinnati Bengals.

2. No Browns quarterback has ever completed 70% of his passes in a season. The most accurate field general to start for a full season was Otto Graham, who came the closest in 1953, when he hit 64.7%.

3. Rookie Tim Couch could have used some better blocking when he became the Browns' quarterback in 1999. He was sacked a whopping 56 times, the highest total in Cleveland history. That's an average of four sacks per start for Couch.

4. Six quarterbacks have played their entire NFL careers with Cleveland. These players range from the first two quarterbacks in Cleveland history, Otto Graham and Cliff Lewis; to brief starters Will Cuerton, Terry Luck, and Johnny Manziel; to franchise icon Brian Sipe. Current quarterback, Baker Mayfield, has not played anywhere else in his three-year NFL career, but it remains to be seen if he will retire as a Brown.

5. Hall of Fame quarterback Otto Graham served the longest tenure as the Browns' starting quarterback. Graham started the majority of Cleveland's games for ten consecutive seasons between 1946 and 1955, including every single game in six of those seasons.

6. Popular Browns quarterback Bernie Kosar was born in Ohio and always supported his home community. In retirement, Kosar purchased an Arena Football League team called the Las Vegas Gladiators and moved the team to Cleveland. Kosar also purchased partial ownership of the National Hockey League's Florida Panthers but was not able to relocate that team to Ohio.

7. Cleveland quarterback Jeff Garcia was inspired to work hard and become a successful football player to make his parents proud. The Garcia family had been tragically affected by the death of Jeff's twin sisters, the drowning death of his brother, and the passing of another sister who was killed in a vehicle accident.

8. Quarterback Vinny Testaverde spent an incredible 21 seasons as an NFL player, including a three-year stint with Cleveland from 1993 to 1995. Thanks to this longevity, Testaverde holds a dubious NFL record: most losses while holding the starting quarterback job. Testaverde was on the losing end 123 times during his career.

9. The legendary Otto Graham was an excellent and avid golfer. Graham not only lived on a golf course but played

in many tournaments, frequently partnering with New York Yankees icon Joe DiMaggio in many of those events.

10. During the NFL Draft in 2014, quarterback Johnny Manziel made his case for the Browns to pick him, text-messaging quarterbacks coach Dowell Loggains to say he would "wreck the league" in Cleveland. Loggains showed the message to head coach Mike Pettine, which prompted Cleveland to trade up and select Manziel 22nd overall.

CHAPTER 5:

THE PASS CATCHERS

QUIZ TIME!

1. Four wide receivers have recorded 50 or more career touchdown catches for the Browns. Which one of them has the most, with 70?

    a. Ray Renfro
    b. Dante Lavelli
    c. Paul Warfield
    d. Gary Collins

2. No one in Browns history is within 250 receptions of tight end Ozzie Newsome at the top of Cleveland's record book.

    a. True
    b. False

3. Who is the Browns' single-season leader in receiving touchdowns scored, with 16?

    a. Tight end Ozzie Newsome
    b. Wide receiver Braylon Edwards

c. Flanker Gary Collins

d. Wide receiver Josh Gordon

4. Who holds the all-time career franchise record for receiving yardage for the Browns?

   a. Right end Dante Lavelli

   b. Wide receiver Webster Slaughter

   c. Tight end Ozzie Newsome

   d. Wide receiver Paul Warfield

5. How did Cleveland receiver Josh Gordon's NFL career come to a premature end?

   a. He suffered a concussion while being tackled out of bounds on a late hit.

   b. He was suspended indefinitely for violating the league's substance abuse policy.

   c. He was arrested for assault and battery and was sentenced to a 10-year prison sentence.

   d. He broke a vertebra while diving into shallow water on vacation and was paralyzed from the waist down.

6. No Brown with at least 100 receptions has averaged 20 yards per catch in his career. Which Cleveland pass catcher came the closest, with a 19.6 yards per catch average?

   a. Wide receiver Ray Renfro

   b. Tight end Ozzie Newsome

   c. Wide receiver Ricky Feacher

   d. Tight end Milt Morin

7. In 2013, Browns wide receiver Josh Gordon put up back-to-back games in which he had 237 receiving yards and 261 receiving yards, respectively.

   a. True
   b. False

8. Which Browns pass catcher played more NFL games with the franchise than any other player?

   a. Wide receiver Ray Renfro
   b. Flanker Gary Collins
   c. Tight end Ozzie Newsome
   d. Wide receiver Paul Warfield

9. Three pass catchers have over 340 career receptions for the Cleveland Browns. Which of the following players is NOT one of them?

   a. Tight end Ozzie Newsome
   b. Right end Dante Lavelli
   c. Left end Mac Speedie
   d. Wide receiver Kevin Johnson

10. Despite playing just four years with the club, flanker Bobby Mitchell has more career fumbles than any other Browns wide receiver. How many times did he cough up the ball?

   a. 14
   b. 19
   c. 27
   d. 32

11. At the end of the 2020 NFL season, the Browns had ten wide receivers under contract for 2021. Which one of those wide receivers had the highest base salary on the team, at $14.5 million?

    a. Jarvis Landry
    b. Rashard Higgins
    c. Odell Beckham Jr.
    d. Donovan Peoples-Jones

12. Browns teammates Eric Metcalf and Reggie Langhorne held a competition each year to see who could record the fewest fumbles during the season. The loser would take the winner out to dinner at a restaurant of the winner's choice, where the loser was deemed not worthy to use his hands while eating their meals.

    a. True
    b. False

13. How many Browns tight ends have caught over 200 passes for the club during their careers?

    a. 1: Ozzie Newsome
    b. 2: Ozzie Newsome and Kellen Winslow Jr.
    c. 3: Ozzie Newsome, Kellen Winslow Jr., and Milt Morin
    d. 5: Ozzie Newsome, Kellen Winslow Jr., Milt Morin, Steve Heiden, and Gary Barnidge

14. Which two teammates posted the highest combined receiving yardage total in a season for the Browns, putting up 2,563 yards between them?

a. Wide receiver Josh Gordon and tight end Jordan Cameron in 2013

b. Wide receiver Braylon Edwards and tight end Kellen Winslow Jr. in 2007

c. Flanker Gary Collins and split end Paul Warfield in 1966

d. Wide receivers Webster Slaughter and Reggie Langhorne in 1989

15. Wide receiver Paul Warfield is a member of the Cleveland Browns Ring of Honor; he also made the Honor Roll of which other NFL team?

a. San Francisco 49ers

b. Green Bay Packers

c. Miami Dolphins

d. Minnesota Vikings

16. Former Browns wide receiver Paul Warfield did some scouting for the team in his retirement and recommended wide receiver Webster Slaughter to general manager Ernie Accorsi. Slaughter starred for the Browns for six seasons before moving on to other teams.

a. True

b. False

17. Cleveland receiver Dante Lavelli was drafted into World War II and missed years of his career while serving in the military. Which of the following famous battles did Lavelli NOT take part in?

a. The D-Day landings at Omaha Beach in France
b. The Battle of the Bulge in Belgium
c. The Siege of Bastogne in Belgium
d. The Battle of Monte Cassino in Italy

18. Which two receivers share the team record with 89 catches in one season?

    a. Wide receivers Paul Warfield and Braylon Edwards
    b. Tight end Ozzie Newsome and wide receiver Webster Slaughter
    c. Wide receiver Jarvis Landry and tight end Gary Barnidge
    d. Tight ends Ozzie Newsome and Kellen Winslow Jr.

19. Which two teammates posted the highest reception total in a season for the Browns, converting 167 passes into catches?

    a. Wide receiver Josh Gordon and tight end Jordan Cameron in 2013
    b. Tight end Ozzie Newsome and running back Greg Pruitt in 1981
    c. Wide receiver Braylon Edwards and tight end Kellen Winslow Jr. in 2007
    d. Wide receivers Jarvis Landry and Odell Beckham Jr. in 2019

20. No players from the twenty-first century are in the top 10 in Cleveland's franchise history for career receiving yards.

    a. True
    b. False

QUIZ ANSWERS

1. D – Gary Collins

2. A – True

3. B – Wide receiver Braylon Edwards

4. C – Tight end Ozzie Newsome

5. B – He was suspended indefinitely for violating the league's substance abuse policy.

6. A – Wide receiver Ray Renfro

7. A – True

8. C – Tight end Ozzie Newsome

9. D – Wide receiver Kevin Johnson

10. A – 14

11. C – Odell Beckham Jr.

12. B – False

13. C – 3: Ozzie Newsome, Kellen Winslow Jr., and Milt Morin

14. A – Wide receiver Josh Gordon and tight end Jordan Cameron in 2013

15. C – Miami Dolphins

16. A – True

17. D – The Battle of Monte Cassino in Italy

18. D – Tight ends Ozzie Newsome and Kellen Winslow Jr.

19. A – Wide receiver Josh Gordon and tight end Jordan Cameron in 2013

20. A – True

DID YOU KNOW?

1. Browns icon Ozzie Newsome ranks eighth on the all-time list of receiving yards by a tight end in NFL history. Every single player ahead of him on the list played later on, in a more wide-open passing era, making Newsome's accomplishments all the more impressive.

2. The single-game record for most receptions in Cleveland Browns history was set in 1984 and matched in 2013. Tight end Ozzie Newsome reeled in 14 passes against the New York Jets and wide receiver Josh Gordon did the same thing nearly 30 years later against the Pittsburgh Steelers.

3. Browns star receiver Paul Warfield was a native Ohioan. He was born in Warren, Ohio, in 1942, attended college at Ohio State University, and played professionally for the Browns. When Cleveland eventually traded him to the Miami Dolphins, where he won two Super Bowls, Warfield was sad to go, saying, "Miami was not a place I desired to go."

4. Kick returner Eric Metcalf was a track star in college, twice winning the NCAA's long jump championship. The versatile Metcalf excelled both as a receiver and a returner and is the only NFL athlete to top 7,000 yards both on offense and on special teams.

5. Cleveland star Mac Speedie excelled with the Browns, making six First Team All-Pro squads, but left the team in 1953 in a contract dispute. Speedie moved on to the Saskatchewan Roughriders of the Canadian Football League and then the BC Lions of the Western Interprovincial Football Union, where he made more money but saw his Pro Football Hall of Fame candidacy suffer. He was not elected until 2020, 27 years after his death.

6. Wide receiver Dante Lavelli had a big game on October 14, 1949, against the Los Angeles Dons. Lavelli reeled in four touchdown passes during a blowout 61-14 Browns win, setting the team's single-game record that still stands.

7. Browns wide receiver Kevin Johnson was a quarterback throughout his high school career and planned to continue in the position. However, at Syracuse University, he could not beat out Donovan McNabb for the job and changed position so as not to be stuck on the bench. Both Johnson and McNabb went on to successful NFL careers at their positions.

8. One year after catching a team-high 16 touchdown passes in 2007, Cleveland wide receiver Braylon Edwards make a public wager with Olympic swimmer Michael Phelps that Edwards would catch 17 touchdowns in 2008. Phelps won the bet easily, as Edwards grabbed only three scores that year though he did lead the league with 23 dropped passes.

9. Dante Lavelli was such a good athlete that he was offered a position with MLB's Detroit Tigers but turned them down to play football for Cleveland instead.

10. Browns legend Ozzie Newsome never left the Cleveland Browns, yet he is a member of the rival Baltimore Ravens. Newsome played tight end for Cleveland from 1978 through 1990, then stepped immediately into the front office in 1991. When the club moved to Baltimore in 1996, Newsome went with them and remains with the Ravens despite Cleveland's re-entry as a franchise in 1999.

CHAPTER 6:

RUNNING WILD

QUIZ TIME!

1. Who holds the Browns' single-season franchise rushing record of 1,863 yards?

   a. Nick Chubb

   b. Peyton Hillis

   c. Jim Brown

   d. Jamal Lewis

2. It is a Browns tradition for every running back to tap his helmet against the helmets of the starting offensive linemen following the pre-game warm-up.

   a. True

   b. False

3. Which running back accumulated the most carries for Cleveland (115 attempts) without ever scoring a rushing touchdown?

   a. Tommy Vardell

   b. Chris Ogbonnaya

c. Montario Hardesty

d. Abdul-Karim al-Jabbar

4. Which of the following is NOT true about legendary Browns running back Jim Brown on the field?

a. He made First Team All-Pro eight times during his career and led the NFL in rushing yards each of those years.

b. He ran even harder when it counted most, with a playoff rushing average almost 30 yards per game higher than his regular-season average.

c. He was voted the NFL's Most Valuable Player three times during his career, including both his rookie season and his final season.

d. He was named to the NFL's All-Time Team when it celebrated its 50th anniversary, 75th anniversary, and 100th anniversary.

5. Which of the following is NOT true about legendary Browns running back Jim Brown off the field?

a. He starred in the classic World War II movie *The Dirty Dozen* alongside Hollywood legends Charles Bronson and Ernest Borgnine.

b. He once posed for a magazine called *Playgirl* that published pictures of Brown displaying full frontal nudity.

c. He was such a force in the game of lacrosse that the rules of the sport were changed to keep Brown from protecting the ball near his body.

d. He owned a lavish mansion in Los Angeles that famously had four swimming pools and a regulation-size football field incorporated into the landscaping.

6. No Browns running back aside from Jim Brown (with at least 30 games played) has averaged over 100 yards per game during his career. Nick Chubb is the closest; what is his yards per game average?

    a. 76.3
    b. 80.8
    c. 91.7
    d. 99.2

7. The incomparable Jim Brown has 106 rushing touchdowns with the Browns, which is more than the next three highest Cleveland running backs combined.

    a. True
    b. False

8. In which season did Browns fullback Marion Motley record an astonishing 8.2 yards per carry for Cleveland?

    a. 1946
    b. 1948
    c. 1951
    d. 1954

9. Which Cleveland running back (with at least 300 carries) has the highest career yards gained per attempt, with 5.7?

    a. Mike Phipps
    b. Bobby Mitchell

c. Jim Brown

d. Marion Motley

10. In 2018, Cleveland running back Nick Chubb recorded his first two NFL rushing touchdowns against which NFL team, during a game in which he carried just three times but still broke 100 yards rushing for the day, becoming only the fourth NFL player ever to do so?

a. Buffalo Bills

b. Jacksonville Jaguars

c. Oakland Raiders

d. Green Bay Packers

11. How many of the Browns' top 10 seasons for rushing touchdowns were recorded by the great Jim Brown?

a. 1

b. 3

c. 5

d. 9

12. Denver Broncos edge rusher Bradley Chubb, who was drafted in 2018, is the cousin of Cleveland Browns running back Nick Chubb, who was also drafted in 2018.

a. True

b. False

13. Which Cleveland running back has the most career fumbles, with 59?

a. Greg Pruitt

b. Jim Brown

c. Mike Pruitt

d. Leroy Kelly

14. Jim Brown had Cleveland's top seven seasons with the highest single-season rushing yards per game marks. In how many of those seasons did Brown average over 100 yards per game?

   a. 1

   b. 3

   c. 5

   d. 7

15. Where did Cleveland coach Paul Brown discover Marion Motley, the Hall of Fame running back who broke the NFL's color barrier in 1946?

   a. Outside Cleveland Stadium, where Motley was a security guard

   b. In college, playing linebacker at the University of Nevada

   c. On a US Navy football team during World War II

   d. Working at a steel mill in Canton, Ohio

16. The Browns' 1st round draft pick, running back William Green once missed most of a season due to a drug suspension. While serving this suspension, Green was stabbed by his wife during an argument and then missed the rest of the season.

   a. True

   b. False

17. During his time in Cleveland, which running back won a fan voting contest to become the athlete featured on the cover of the popular *Madden* video game series?

    a. Trent Richardson
    b. Peyton Hillis
    c. Willis McGahee
    d. Kareem Hunt

18. Which of the following is NOT a workplace that employed star Browns running back Marion Motley after his playing career ended?

    a. Kentucky Fried Chicken
    b. The Ohio Lottery
    c. Harry Miller Excavating
    d. The United States Postal Service

19. How many running backs have carried the ball over 1,000 times for the Browns?

    a. 1: Leroy Kelly
    b. 2: Jim Brown and Earnest Byner
    c. 4: Leroy Kelly, Greg Pruitt, Marion Motley, and Nick Chubb
    d. 5: Jim Brown, Leroy Kelly, Greg Pruitt, Mike Pruitt, and Kevin Mack

20. During the early years of the AAFC, star Browns running back Marion Motley avoided playing in one game in Miami because of racially motivated death threats against him.

a. True

b. False

QUIZ ANSWERS

1. C – Jim Brown

2. B – False

3. D – Abdul-Karim al-Jabbar

4. B – He ran even harder when it counted most, with a playoff rushing average almost 30 yards per game higher than his regular-season average.

5. D – He owned a lavish mansion in Los Angeles that famously had four swimming pools and a regulation-size football field incorporated into the landscaping.

6. B – 80.8

7. B – False

8. A – 1946

9. D – Marion Motley

10. C – Oakland Raiders

11. C – 5

12. A – True

13. A – Greg Pruitt

14. D – 7

15. C – On a US Navy football team during World War II

16. A – True

17. B – Peyton Hillis

18. A – Kentucky Fried Chicken

19. D – 5: Jim Brown, Leroy Kelly, Greg Pruitt, Mike Pruitt, and Kevin Mack

20. A – True

DID YOU KNOW?

1. Four running backs who have played for the Browns have been enshrined in the Pro Football Hall of Fame. Jim Brown, Marion Motley, Leroy Kelly, and Bobby Mitchell all made the cut. Mitchell split time between running back and wide receiver but did have over 400 carries with Cleveland.

2. During the late 1970s and early 1980s, the Cleveland Browns employed both Greg Pruitt and Mike Pruitt at running back. The Pruitts were unrelated; Greg hailed from Houston, Texas, and Mike from Chicago, Illinois.

3. Ten times in NFL history, a running back has scored 20 or more rushing touchdowns in a single season. No Browns player has accomplished the feat. The closest was superstar Jim Brown, who notched 17 rushing touchdowns in both 1958 and 1965.

4. Cleveland superstar Jim Brown is the only running back in NFL history to finish his playing career with a rushing average of over 100 yards per game. Brown's record average is 104.3 rushing yards per game; which many consider unbreakable.

5. At the University of Tennessee, future Browns running back Jamal Lewis completed a pass to his college quarterback, future Pro Football Hall-of-Famer Peyton Manning.

6. Browns running back Jim Brown led a tumultuous life off the field. He has been engaged to three different women, marrying two, and been arrested at least seven times in his life, on charges ranging from vandalism to attempted murder. Only twice was he convicted and sentenced, though, both times on charges that were less serious.

7. After Jim Brown retired in 1965, Cleveland targeted free agent running back Nick Pietrosante as a replacement. Pietrosante was signed away from the Detroit Lions but could not live up to Brown's accomplishments and retired after just two mediocre seasons in Cleveland.

8. Although Pietrosante failed as Jim Brown's replacement, it turned out that Cleveland already had an incredible option on their roster. Leroy Kelly, who had been Brown's backup, took over the position, making six Pro Bowls and leading the NFL in rushing yards twice. Kelly went on to be elected to the Pro Football Hall of Fame.

9. The longest rushing touchdown in Browns history belongs to current running back Nick Chubb. Chubb broke off a 92-yard run for a score in a 2018 win over the Atlanta Falcons, eclipsing Bobby Mitchell's 90-yard rush for Cleveland in 1959.

10. Cleveland Browns running back Dub Jones owns a share of the NFL record for most touchdowns in a single game, with six. Jones torched the Chicago Bears for four rushing touchdowns and two receiving scores in 1951. The mark has only been equaled twice, by the Bears' Gale Sayers in

1965, and not again until 2020 when Alvin Kamara of the New Orleans Saints matched the feat.

CHAPTER 7:

IN THE TRENCHES

QUIZ TIME!

1. Which Browns defender holds the team record with four sacks in a game?

    a. Defensive end Myles Garrett

    b. Defensive end Kenard Lang

    c. Linebacker Andra Davis

    d. Defensive tackle Gerard Warren

2. The 2016 Cleveland Browns hold the NFL record for the heaviest combined weight of all starting offensive and defensive linemen.

    a. True

    b. False

3. Who is the Browns' all-time franchise leader in sacks, with 62?

    a. Linebacker Clay Matthews Jr.

    b. Defensive end Myles Garrett

    c. Defensive tackle Michael Dean Perry

    d. Defensive end Rob Burnett

4. Which offensive lineman did the Browns select highest in the NFL Entry Draft, using a 3ʳᵈ overall pick to add the stout blocker to their team?

   a. Tackle Jedrick Wills Jr.
   b. Guard Pete Adams
   c. Center Kurt Burris
   d. Tackle Joe Thomas

5. Which offensive lineman has played more games on the offensive side of the Browns' line of scrimmage than anyone else, with 203?

   a. Tackle Doug Dieken
   b. Guard Gene Hickerson
   c. Tackle Joe Thomas
   d. Center Tom DeLeone

6. Which defensive lineman has played more games on the defensive side of the Browns' line of scrimmage than anyone else?

   a. Tackle Jerry Sherk
   b. End Paul Wiggin
   c. Tackle Walter Johnson
   d. End Orpheus Roy

7. Standout Browns defensive tackle Michael Dean Perry was the brother of Chicago Bears defensive tackle and pop culture icon William "the Refrigerator" Perry.

   a. True
   b. False

8. Which Browns defender had the most career forced fumbles, with 24?

    a. Linebacker Mike Johnson

    b. Linebacker Clay Matthews Jr.

    c. Defensive end Myles Garrett

    d. Defensive end Jabaal Sheard

9. Quarterback Brian Sipe tops the record books for most fumbles recovered for the Browns, but he tended to be cleaning up his own mess. Which two defenders have created the most turnovers for Cleveland by scooping up an opponent's fumble?

    a. Defensive ends Len Ford and Paul Wiggin

    b. Linebacker Galen Fiss and defensive tackle Jerry Sherk

    c. Linebacker Clay Matthews Jr. and defensive tackle Don Colo

    d. Safety Stevon Moore and defensive end Rob Burnett

10. Lineman Gene Hickerson played his entire NFL career with the Cleveland Browns after they made him a 7th round selection in 1957. How long did that career last?

    a. 9 seasons

    b. 11 seasons

    c. 15 seasons

    d. 19 seasons

11. Browns mainstay left tackle Joe Thomas played over 165 NFL games with the club. Where does he rank in games played all time for Cleveland?

a. 1st

b. 3rd

c. 7th

d. 12th

12. Famous talk show hostess Kathie Lee Gifford named her son Cody after Browns offensive tackle Cody Risien, whom she saw playing on television while she was pregnant. In a strange coincidence, Cody Risien and Cody Gifford happen to share the same birthday.

a. True

b. False

13. Which current Browns defensive lineman has the longest tenure in Cleveland?

a. Defensive tackle Malik Jackson

b. Defensive end Joe Jackson

c. Defensive end Myles Garrett

d. Defensive tackle Andrew Billings

14. Which of the following facts about Browns offensive lineman Dick Schafrath is NOT true?

a. He was the last person voted the team's Most Valuable Player before the Browns did away with the award.

b. He married Ginger Martin, a model who was a runner-up in the Miss America Pageant.

c. He was one of the first NFL players to include weightlifting as part of his training and bulked up 50 pounds after being drafted by Cleveland.

d. He once paddled a canoe across Lake Erie without any breaks for rest.

15. Which lineman did NFL.com declare as the "third greatest Cleveland Brown of all time"?

    a. Defensive tackle Michael Dean Perry
    b. Defensive end Myles Garrett
    c. Left tackle Joe Thomas
    d. Nose tackle Bob Golic

16. During his high school career, future Browns left tackle Joe Thomas played right tackle, tight end, fullback, and defensive end for the Brookfield Central Lancers. He also handled kickoff, field goal, and punting duties for the team.

    a. True
    b. False

17. Excellent Browns guard Joe DeLamielleure blocked for quarterback Brian Sipe during Sipe's MVP season in 1980. This was the second time DeLamielleure had blocked for an NFL MVP; who was the first player he helped find the pinnacle of success?

    a. San Diego Chargers quarterback Dan Fouts
    b. Houston Oilers running back Earl Campbell
    c. Buffalo Bills running back O.J. Simpson
    d. Oakland Raiders quarterback Ken Stabler

18. Browns left tackle Joe Thomas went to the Pro Bowl for the first five years of his career, a feat matched by only one other NFL offensive lineman. Which one?

   a. Tackle Walter Jones of the Seattle Seahawks
   b. Guard Quentin Nelson of the Indianapolis Colts
   c. Guard Nate Newton of the Dallas Cowboys
   d. Tackle Richmond Webb of the Miami Dolphins

19. Which of the following statements about Hall of Fame Browns guard Gene Hickerson is NOT true?

   a. He earned First Team All-Pro selections for five straight years for his run blocking after legendary running back Jim Brown retired from football.
   b. He signed an endorsement deal to represent Players cigarettes after he had given up smoking to improve his conditioning.
   c. He played an entire decade of NFL football without missing a game after breaking his leg twice in one season and missing most of the year.
   d. He was honored with a "GH" sticker on the team's helmets during the 2008 season after he had passed away earlier in the year.

20. Cleveland defensive tackle Larry Ogunjobi has a degree in astrophysics and works part time for NASA during the NFL offseason.

   a. True
   b. False

QUIZ ANSWERS

1. C – Linebacker Andra Davis

2. B – False

3. A – Linebacker Clay Matthews Jr.

4. D – Tackle Joe Thomas

5. A – Tackle Doug Dieken

6. C – Tackle Walter Johnson

7. A – True

8. B – Linebacker Clay Matthews Jr.

9. A – Defensive ends Len Ford and Paul Wiggin

10. C – 15 seasons

11. D – 12th

12. A – True

13. C – Defensive end Myles Garrett

14. B – He married Ginger Martin, a model who was a runner-up in the Miss America Pageant.

15. C – Left tackle Joe Thomas

16. A – True

17. C – Buffalo Bills running back O.J. Simpson

18. D – Tackle Richmond Webb of the Miami Dolphins

19. B – He signed an endorsement deal to represent Players cigarettes after he had given up smoking to improve his conditioning.

20. B – False

DID YOU KNOW?

1. Twenty players share the Cleveland record for most safeties created, as nobody in franchise history has done it more than once. Fourteen defensive linemen own a piece of that record, which is easily more than any other position group.

2. Browns franchise left tackle Joe Thomas holds the NFL record for longest streak of consecutive snaps played. The league began tracking this statistic in 1999, and Thomas recorded an incredible 10,363 straight snaps, despite the physical demands of his position.

3. Offensive tackle Doug Dieken has been involved with the Cleveland Browns for 40 years. Dieken began playing for the team in 1971 and retired in 1984 to become the team's radio broadcaster. Dieken has held that position ever since, except for a three-year period when the team briefly ceased to exist after its move to Baltimore. During this interlude, Dieken was still an official spokesperson and ambassador for the Browns.

4. Browns defensive end Myles Garrett has an unusual interest that he pursues in his spare time: paleontology. During road trips, Garrett often visits museums to indulge in his hobby, and he corresponds with scientific experts whom he considers among his friends. Garrett is

in the process of writing a book about dinosaurs for children during his spare time.

5. Defensive tackle Walter Johnson played for over a decade with Cleveland and also had an interesting second career as a professional wrestler. Johnson wrestled mostly with a promotion called New Japan Pro Wrestling, along with fellow NFL player Ron Pritchard, a linebacker for the Cincinnati Bengals.

6. Center Alex Mack was drafted by the Browns in 2009 and quickly became a stalwart. Mack did not miss a game through the first five seasons of his career. In 2014, he signed a rich, $42 million free-agent deal with the Jacksonville Jaguars. Cleveland considered Mack highly valuable and matched the offer to keep him. A few months later, bad luck finally struck, as Mack broke his leg and missed most of the 2014 NFL season.

7. During a Week 11 game against the Pittsburgh Steelers in 2019, Cleveland defensive end Myles Garrett put a late hit on Steelers quarterback Mason Rudolph, knocking him to the ground. Garrett then ripped off Rudolph's helmet and eventually hit Rudolph in the face with that helmet. For these actions, Garrett was fined over $45,000 and suspended for the remainder of the season. This suspension was the second-longest in NFL history for an action that happened during a game.

8. Offensive lineman Dick Schafrath spent his whole life in Ohio. Schafrath was born in Wooster, Ohio, attended

Ohio State University, played over a decade in the NFL with the Cleveland Browns, and then became a member of the Ohio State Senate for over 15 years after his playing career concluded.

9. The Houston brothers, Lin and Jim, both made it to the NFL, and both played their entire careers with the Cleveland Browns. Despite this, they never played together. Older brother Lin played guard for the club from 1946 to 1953, and the younger Jim began as a defensive tackle with Cleveland in 1960, lasting with the team until 1972.

10. Browns defensive tackle Michael Dean Perry once had a sandwich named after him at the popular McDonald's fast-food restaurant chains in Cleveland. The "MDP" included three burger patties, cheese, and bacon, and was the largest sandwich on the menu.

CHAPTER 8:

THE BACK SEVEN

QUIZ TIME!

1. Which Browns defensive back is the franchise's all-time leader in interceptions, with 45?

   a. Cornerback Clarence Scott

   b. Free safety Felix Wright

   c. Free safety Thom Darden

   d. Cornerback Joe Haden

2. During the 2010s poker craze, members of Cleveland's secondary and linebacking corps held a weekly game where, rather than playing for money, the losers had to tweet embarrassing things about themselves or flattering things about the winners.

   a. True

   b. False

3. One Browns defensive player became a major threat with the ball, recording the most interceptions returned for a touchdown, with five. Who was he?

a. Defensive back Warren Lahr

b. Cornerback Bernie Parrish

c. Linebacker Karlos Dansby

d. Safety Eric Turner

4. Although sacks are usually not a high priority for defensive backs in most coaching systems, one Browns defensive back could get to the quarterback when tasked to do so, putting up seven sacks in his Cleveland career. Who did this?

a. Safety Chris Crocker

b. Safety Brodney Pool

c. Cornerback Daylon McCutcheon

d. Cornerback Don Griffin

5. The initials in popular Browns safety T.J. Ward's name stand for what?

a. Thomas Jackson

b. Tony Jamal

c. Tiger Jaws

d. Terrell Jr.

6. Which Browns defender led the team in tackles during the 2020 season, with 59 solo tackles and 91 total tackles?

a. Linebacker B.J. Goodson

b. Defensive end Myles Garrett

c. Safety Andrew Sendejo

d. Cornerback Denzel Ward

7. Three generations (Clay Matthews Sr., Clay Matthews Jr., and Clay Matthews III) of one family all played linebacker in the NFL for the Cleveland Browns.

   a. True
   b. False

8. To which of the following Halls of Fame does talented Browns linebacker Walt Michaels NOT belong?

   a. Virginia Sports Hall of Fame
   b. National Polish American Sports Hall of Fame
   c. Suffolk Sports Hall of Fame on Long Island – Baseball Category
   d. Pro Football Hall of Fame

9. Star Browns linebacker Mike Johnson belonged to all of the following USFL teams except which one before excelling in Cleveland?

   a. Pittsburgh Maulers
   b. Philadelphia Stars
   c. San Antonio Gunslingers
   d. Baltimore Stars

10. Longtime Browns cornerback Joe Haden notched his first career NFL interception against which opposing quarterback?

   a. Jeff Garcia of the San Francisco 49ers
   b. Ben Roethlisberger of the Pittsburgh Steelers
   c. David Garrard of the Jacksonville Jaguars
   d. Chad Henne of the Miami Dolphins

11. Browns mainstay Clarence Scott played 186 NFL games with the club. Where does he rank in games played all time for Cleveland?

    a. 3rd
    b. Tied for 5th
    c. 6th
    d. 8th

12. Years after his playing and coaching careers were both over, Cleveland linebacker Clay Matthews Jr. became a professor of geometry at the University of Southern California.

    a. True
    b. False

13. Which of the following positions has popular Browns cornerback Hanford Dixon NOT held in Cleveland after retiring from his playing career?

    a. Football analyst on the television channel of the local CBS affiliate
    b. Defensive backs assistant coach for the Cleveland Browns
    c. Color commentator for local high school football games on Fox Sports Ohio
    d. Head coach of the Cleveland Crush in the Lingerie Football League

14. Which of these current Browns players has been with the team for three seasons, the longest current tenure in Cleveland's back seven?

a. Cornerback Denzel Ward

b. Linebacker Malcolm Smith

c. Cornerback Troy Hill

d. Safety Grant Delpit

15. Which of the following facts about Browns safety Thom Darden is NOT true?

a. Darden led the NFL in interceptions during the 1978 season.

b. Darden is the only Browns player to score multiple defensive touchdowns in the NFL playoffs.

c. Darden became a successful sports agent in his retirement, representing both NFL and NBA players.

d. Darden put in a bid to buy the Cleveland Browns franchise when it re-entered the league in 1998.

16. In 1965, Bernie Parrish established the Cleveland Cornerback Connection, wherein he donated his gold pocket watch upon retirement to the next cornerback to take up the mantle for Cleveland. To this day, the watch hangs in a cornerback's locker, and he must pass it on if he retires, is traded, cut, or signs elsewhere.

a. True

b. False

17. Since the NFL began officially recording the statistic in 1994, which Cleveland player recorded the most tackles in a single season, with 116?

a. Linebacker Wali Rainer in 1999

b. Linebacker Andra Davis in 2003

c. Linebacker Pepper Johnson in 1995

d. Linebacker D'Qwell Jackson in 2011

18. How did former Browns linebacker John Garlington die in the line of duty while serving as a Wildlife Enforcement Agent in his post-NFL career?

    a. He drowned in a reservoir while patrolling the area for security.

    b. He was shot while pursuing a poacher hunting illegally in a protected area.

    c. He was trapped while battling a forest fire after the wind shifted unexpectedly.

    d. He was mauled by a bear during an attempt to save two trapped campers.

19. Which player's family once appeared (and won) on the popular television game show *Family Feud*?

    a. Safety Eric Turner and his family

    b. Cornerback Joe Haden and his family

    c. Linebacker Clay Matthews Jr. and his family

    d. Linebacker Christian Kirksey and his family

20. Five-time Pro Bowl linebacker Walt Michaels was drafted by the Browns, traded to the Green Bay Packers before playing a single game with Cleveland, and then traded back to the Browns the following year.

    a. True

    b. False

QUIZ ANSWERS

1. C – Free safety Thom Darden

2. B – False

3. A – Defensive back Warren Lahr

4. C – Cornerback Daylon McCutcheon

5. D – Terrell Jr.

6. A – Linebacker B.J. Goodson

7. B – False

8. D – Pro Football Hall of Fame

9. C – San Antonio Gunslingers

10. B – Ben Roethlisberger of the Pittsburgh Steelers

11. D – 8th

12. B – False

13. B – Defensive backs assistant coach for the Cleveland Browns

14. A – Cornerback Denzel Ward

15. B – Darden is the only Browns player to score multiple defensive touchdowns in the NFL playoffs.

16. B – False

17. D – Linebacker D'Qwell Jackson in 2011

18. A – He drowned in a reservoir while patrolling the area for security.

19. C – Linebacker Clay Matthews Jr. and his family

20. A – True

DID YOU KNOW?

1. Passes defended is a stat that the NFL began using at the turn of the century. Cornerback Joe Haden has dominated the statistic for the Browns, having almost twice as many as his closest competitor, cornerback Daylon McCutcheon. Hayden had 101, while McCutcheon finished with 53.

2. Cleveland linebacker Jim Houston is one of the lucky few players to win a high school state championship, a college national championship, and an NFL championship. Houston managed all of these feats within his home state of Ohio, making his triple crown achievement even rarer.

3. Linebacker Clay Matthews Jr. is the all-time leading tackler for the Browns franchise. Matthews played in Cleveland for 16 seasons and racked up 1,430 tackles during that time. He also spent time with the Atlanta Falcons and is the third leading tackler in NFL history.

4. Cleveland linebacker Walt Michaels can count himself among many people to hear Donald Trump say, "You're fired." Before Trump became a reality television star or the president of the United States, he owned the USFL's New Jersey Generals franchise, which Michaels coached in 1984-85. Trump let Michaels go despite a 25-11 record during those two seasons.

5. In his retirement, star Browns safety Bernie Parrish wrote a book titled *They Call It a Game*. Publishing the memoirs

of his playing career was not out of the ordinary, but Parrish came under fire because of allegations in his book that the NFL was guilty of fixing the outcome of some of its games.

6. Browns linebacker Andra Davis's production fluctuated wildly. Davis is the sixth leading career tackler for the Browns but put up totals between 2004 and 2006 that showed his unpredictability: 89 tackles, 199 tackles, 104 tackles.

7. Three back-seven players who have played for the Browns have been enshrined in the Football Hall of Fame. Interestingly, none of the three were inducted based on their play but were each chosen for their success as coaches. They are Don Shula, who coached the Miami Dolphins for over 25 years, and Chuck Knoll and Bill Cowher, who roamed the Pittsburgh Steelers sidelines for over 35 years, combined.

8. Former Browns cornerback Daylon McCutcheon made an incredible leap in his post-playing career in 2015. McCutcheon had been a defensive coordinator at La Puente High School in California when he was hired from that level directly to become an assistant defensive backs coach with the New York Jets.

9. Cleveland safety Eric Turner was explosive on the field, with interception returns of 93 and 94 yards, both for touchdowns. Sadly, Turner retired in 1999 and passed

away from stomach cancer in 2000, when he was just 31 years old.

10. Browns cornerback Joe Haden is one of five brothers whose names all begin with the letter "J." Joe, Josh, Jordan, and Jonathan played college football at four different institutions. Jacob Haden is the only non-football player of the bunch, while Joe Haden was the only brother to make it to the NFL.

CHAPTER 9:

WHERE'D THEY COME FROM?

QUIZ TIME!

1. Where was legendary Browns running back Jim Brown born?

   a. Manhasset, New York

   b. Cleveland, Ohio

   c. St. Simons Island, Georgia

   d. Tyler, Texas

2. Browns running back Marion Motley, who played for several years with the team, was elected to the Pro Football Hall of Fame in Canton, Ohio, which was Motley's hometown.

   a. True

   b. False

3. In 1958, the Browns chose three players from the same college, all of whom lined up on the offensive side of the ball. Where did these three go to school?

   a. University of Alabama

   b. University of Michigan

c. Ohio State University

d. Duke University

4. From which of these NCAA powerhouse programs have the Cleveland Browns never selected a player in the 1st round?

a. University of Alabama

b. University of Michigan

c. University of Notre Dame

d. Clemson University

5. From which team did the Browns acquire useful wide receiver Jarvis Landry in a 2018 swap?

a. New York Giants

b. Miami Dolphins

c. Arizona Cardinals

d. New Orleans Saints

6. Which of the following is NOT a college program that Cleveland drafted a player from during the 1991 NFL Draft?

a. University of Northern Iowa

b. Henderson State University

c. Southeast Missouri State University

d. Central Florida University

7. The Browns have drafted one more player from the Michigan State Spartans than from the Michigan Wolverines.

a. True

b. False

8. Which defensive player, dealt in a trade from the Browns to the Chicago Bears franchise for draft picks (after allegedly burping disrespectfully during a team meeting), is in the Hall of Fame?

    a. Linebacker Dick Butkus
    b. Defensive end Doug Atkins
    c. Defensive tackle Dan Hampton
    d. Linebacker Bronco Nagurski

9. One of the Browns' best trades saw them acquire quarterback Frank Ryan, who made three Pro Bowls and led Cleveland to a championship, in exchange for Larry Stephens, a 3rd round draft pick, and a 6th round draft pick. Which team regretted making that deal with Cleveland?

    a. Los Angeles Rams
    b. Dallas Cowboys
    c. Pittsburgh Steelers
    d. Minnesota Vikings

10. In which city that shares its name with many males was Browns franchise quarterback Baker Mayfield born in 1995?

    a. Tyler, Texas
    b. Warren, Michigan
    c. Eugene, Oregon
    d. Austin, Texas

11. Which two players were teammates in college with the Louisiana State University Tigers before taking the field together in Cleveland?

a. Tight end Kellen Winslow Jr. and running back Duke Johnson

b. Left tackle Joe Thomas and linebacker D'Qwell Jackson

c. Wide receivers Jarvis Landry and Odell Beckham Jr.

d. Quarterback Brandon Weeden and cornerback Joe Haden

12. Cleveland has never in its history completed a trade with its biggest division rival, the Pittsburgh Steelers.

a. True

b. False

13. In 2008, the Browns traded a 2nd round pick to the Green Bay Packers for defensive tackle Corey Williams. After two years of service with Cleveland, they dealt Williams to the Detroit Lions in 2010. Which piece(s) did they receive in return?

a. A 1st round draft pick

b. Guard Garrett Gilkey and a 3rd round draft pick

c. Punter Andy Lee and a 2nd round draft pick

d. A 5th round draft pick

14. In 1959, the Browns drafted defensive tackle Jim Prestel, who played for the University of Idaho, in the 6th round. What was his college team's unusual, criminal-sounding nickname?

a. The Vandals

b. The Killers

c. The Assault

d. The Hooligans

15. The overall pick in 1982, Chip Banks was the highest a linebacker had ever been taken by Cleveland. Banks played college football for which program before coming to the Browns?

a. University of Miami Hurricanes

b. University of Oklahoma Sooners

c. University of Southern California Trojans

d. University of Florida Gators

16. In their entire history, the Browns have never traded away a player who was born in the state of Ohio.

a. True

b. False

17. Only one prestigious Ivy League college program has produced any NFL starters for the Browns when they have dipped into those institutions during the NFL Draft. Which academically strong institution yielded fruit on the field for Cleveland as well?

a. Harvard University

b. Yale University

c. Columbia University

d. Princeton University

18. From which rival team did the Browns poach star linebacker Jamir Miller as a free agent in 1999, giving Cleveland its first Pro Bowl player since re-entering the league after the franchise's move to Baltimore in 1996?

a. New England Patriots
b. Baltimore Ravens
c. Arizona Cardinals
d. Seattle Seahawks

19. The talented and popular Bernie Kosar was the quarterback of which college squad before his time on the field with the Browns?

a. Ohio State University Buckeyes
b. Auburn University Tigers
c. Purdue University Boilermakers
d. University of Miami Hurricanes

20. Cleveland has completed more trades with the in-state rival Cincinnati Bengals than with any other NFL franchise.

a. True
b. False

QUIZ ANSWERS

1. C – St. Simons Island, Georgia

2. A – True

3. D – Duke University

4. D – Clemson University

5. B – Miami Dolphins

6. C – Southeast Missouri State University

7. A – True

8. B – Defensive end Doug Atkins

9. A – Los Angeles Rams

10. D – Austin, Texas

11. C – Wide receivers Jarvis Landry and Odell Beckham Jr.

12. B – False

13. D – A 5th round draft pick

14. A – The Vandals

15. C – University of Southern California Trojans

16. B – False

17. D – Princeton University

18. C – Arizona Cardinals

19. D – University of Miami Hurricanes

20. B – False

DID YOU KNOW?

1. When the Kansas City Chiefs needed to cut NFL rushing leader Kareem Hunt in 2018 because of a video showing Hunt participating in an assault, many other teams kept tabs on Hunt because of his obvious talent. Cleveland signed Hunt a few months later, waited while he served his suspension, and has benefitted from his skill on the field ever since.

2. Cleveland running back Nick Chubb, who is named after his great-grandfather, hails from Chubbtown, Georgia, which was also named after his great-grandfather (along with his seven brothers). The town was a fascinating place that allowed southern black people to live free from slavery even before and during the Civil War.

3. The Browns and Baltimore Ravens have had a fairly heated rivalry throughout their existence, which is natural, considering that Browns owner Art Modell once moved the franchise away from Cleveland to Baltimore. The two teams have not connected on a trade in the past decade.

4. One of the most polarizing free-agent signings made by the Browns occurred in 2007 when they added running back Jamal Lewis from the Baltimore Ravens. Some fans wanted nothing to do with anyone from Baltimore because of the franchise's previous move, while others

relished the opportunity to steal such a good player away from their hated rivals.

5. Cleveland quarterback Baker Mayfield had quite a college career before being picked by the Browns. Mayfield started as a walk-on at Texas Tech University, went through a contentious transfer to the University of Oklahoma, and then won the Heisman Trophy as college football's best player, becoming the first walk-on player ever to accomplish that feat.

6. In a decision that was very unusual at the time, Cleveland chose UCLA safety Eric Turner with the 2nd overall pick in the 1991 NFL Draft. This was (and remains) the highest a defensive back had ever been selected in the draft. His value was proven, though, as Turner went to two Pro Bowls and led the Browns to having the top-ranked defense in the league in 1994.

7. One of the largest and most impactful sets of trades ever made by the Browns was completed in 1977-78 with the Chicago Bears and Los Angeles Rams. Cleveland sent quarterback Mike Phipps to Chicago and received two draft picks in the blockbuster. One of those draft picks became iconic linebacker Clay Matthews Jr., and the other was dealt to Los Angeles for a different pick, which the Browns used on Hall of Fame tight end Ozzie Newsome.

8. Current fan-favorite defensive tackle Larry Ogunjobi is the only player the Browns have ever selected who played in college for the University of North Carolina at Charlotte 49ers.

9. During the 2012 NCAA season, future Browns quarterback Johnny Manziel had an incredible season for the Texas A&M Aggies. Manziel passed for over 3,000 yards, rushed for over 1,000 yards, and won the Manning Award, the Davey O'Brien National Quarterback Award, and the Heisman Trophy, becoming the first freshman ever to claim any of those honors.

10. Cleveland hit the jackpot when they selected center Frank Winters from Western Illinois University in 1987. The little-scouted school paid off in this instance, as Winters played 231 games with the Browns after being taken in the 10th round.

CHAPTER 10:

IN THE DRAFT ROOM

QUIZ TIME!

1. The first Browns draft choice ever, halfback Ken Carpenter, attended Oregon State University, where he played for the football team that went by which nickname?

   a. Beavers
   b. Ducks
   c. Timberwolves
   d. Lumberjacks

2. For four consecutive years in the 1980s, the Browns traded out of the 1st round of the NFL Draft, acquiring more proven talent to compete with the Denver Broncos.

   a. True
   b. False

3. From which of the following college football programs have the Browns drafted the most players?

   a. Texas Longhorns
   b. Texas Tech Red Riders

c. Texas A&M Aggies

d. Texas-El Paso Miners

4. During the 1st round of the 2020 NFL Draft, Cleveland congratulated which of the following players on becoming a Brown remotely, via webcam, because the COVID-19 pandemic prevented the usual handshakes on stage?

a. Cornerback Greedy Williams of LSU

b. Quarterback Baker Mayfield of Oklahoma

c. Defensive back Greg Newsome II of Northwestern

d. Offensive tackle Jedrick Wills Jr. of Alabama

5. The Browns selected two defensive teammates from the Louisiana State University Tigers in the 2020 NFL Draft. Which teammates did they choose with the 44th and 97th picks?

a. Defensive tackle Jordan Elliott and linebacker Jacob Phillips

b. Safety Grant Delpit and linebacker Jacob Phillips

c. Cornerbacks Greedy Williams and Donnie Lewis

d. Cornerback Greedy Williams and safety Grant Delpit

6. How many times in history has Cleveland used a top 10 overall draft pick?

a. 17

b. 22

c. 29

d. 36

7. The Browns have never held the 1st overall pick in the NFL Draft in the entire history of the franchise.

   a. True
   b. False

8. Quarterback Tim Couch was drafted by the Browns out of which school that is better known as a basketball powerhouse than a football school?

   a. Duke University
   b. University of Kentucky
   c. University of Kansas
   d. University of North Carolina

9. Couch was drafted by Cleveland 1st overall in the 1999 NFL Entry Draft. Which excellent quarterback selected with the 2nd overall pick went on to record more than three times the completions, passing yards, and passing touchdowns of Couch?

   a. Daunte Culpepper of the Minnesota Vikings
   b. Akili Smith of the Cincinnati Bengals
   c. Donovan McNabb of the Philadelphia Eagles
   d. Chad Pennington of the New York Jets

10. Only two Ivy League players have played for the Browns after being drafted by them. Which intelligent players made it with Cleveland?

   a. Defensive tackle Carl Barisich and tight end Seth DeValve
   b. Wide receiver Webster Slaughter and defensive back Coye Francies

c. Linebacker Sid Williams and defensive end Paul Wiggin

d. Halfback Billy Gault and kicker George Hunt

11. How high did Cleveland select running back Duke Johnson in the 2015 NFL Entry Draft?

a. 1st round, 6th overall

b. 2nd round, 39th overall

c. 3rd round, 77th overall

d. 7th round, 224th overall

12. Due in part to their longstanding rivalry with the Pittsburgh Steelers, Cleveland has never drafted a player from the University of Pittsburgh.

a. True

b. False

13. How many draft choices did the Browns give up to the Minnesota Vikings to move up from 4th overall to 3rd overall and select running back Trent Richardson in the 2012 NFL Draft?

a. One 1st round and one 7th round pick

b. One 1st round, one 5th round, and one 7th round pick

c. Three 2nd round picks

d. One 1st round, one 4th round, one 5th round, and one 7th round pick

14. Defensive back and future Hall-of-Famer Don Shula played four years of college ball for which program before being drafted by the Browns?

a. John Carroll University

b. University of Minnesota

c. New Mexico State University

d. Texas Christian University

15. The Browns drafted two players from Syracuse University who went on to play more than 180 NFL games each. Who were these players?

a. Tackle John Brown and wide receiver Kevin Johnson

b. Running back Jim Brown and linebacker Cliff Odom

c. Kicker Don Cockroft and defensive end Anthony Pleasant

d. Guard Walt Sweeney and defensive end Rob Burnett

16. Cleveland running back Jim Brown was such a talented athlete coming out of college that he was drafted in not one but three sports (basketball, baseball, and football).

a. True

b. False

17. Which team did the Browns trade up with so they could select linebacker D'Qwell Jackson in the 2nd round at the NFL Draft in 2006?

a. Indianapolis Colts

b. Tampa Bay Buccaneers

c. New Orleans Saints

d. Green Bay Packers

18. In the 1976 NFL Draft, Cleveland selected two quarterbacks. Who were they?

a. Vinny Testaverde and Bernie Kosar

b. Mark Miller and Paul McDonald

c. Gene Swick and Craig Nagel

d. Brian Sipe and Randy Mattingly

19. Which players did the Cleveland Browns select with their three 1st round draft picks in 2017?

a. Defensive end Myles Garrett, safety Jabrill Peppers, and tight end David Njoku

b. Quarterback Baker Mayfield, cornerback Denzel Ward, and defensive tackle Larry Ogunjobi

c. Wide receiver Corey Coleman, quarterback DeShone Kizer, and defensive end Emmanuel Ogbah

d. Defensive tackle Danny Shelton, center Cameron Erving, and cornerback Justin Gilbert

20. Between 1999 and 2013, Cleveland enjoyed a stretch in which they selected at least one player each year who lasted at least 100 games in the NFL.

a. True

b. False

QUIZ ANSWERS

1. A – Beavers

2. B – False

3. C – Texas A&M Aggies

4. D – Offensive tackle Jedrick Wills Jr. of Alabama

5. B – Safety Grant Delpit and linebacker Jacob Phillips

6. C – 29

7. B – False

8. B – University of Kentucky

9. C – Donovan McNabb of the Philadelphia Eagles

10. A – Defensive tackle Carl Barisich and tight end Seth DeValve

11. C – 3rd round, 77th overall

12. B – False

13. D – One 1st round, one 4th round, one 5th round, and one 7th round pick

14. A – John Carroll University

15. D – Guard Walt Sweeney and defensive end Rob Burnett

16. B – False

17. C – New Orleans Saints

18. C – Gene Swick and Craig Nagel

19. A – Defensive end Myles Garrett, safety Jabrill Peppers, and tight end David Njoku

20. A – True

DID YOU KNOW?

1. Defensive end Myles Garrett, who was chosen 1ˢᵗ overall in 2017, is the highest drafted player ever selected from Texas A&M University. Garrett is one of five 1ˢᵗ overall draft picks in Browns history.

2. The most players Cleveland has drafted from any school is 35. This mark is held by Ohio State University and includes two Pro Football Hall-of-Famers in wide receiver Paul Warfield and defensive back Dick LeBeau.

3. When the 2007 NFL Draft was approaching, offensive tackle Joe Thomas knew that he would be selected very high out of the University of Wisconsin. The unassuming Thomas did not care and passed on attending the draft to go fishing with his father. When Cleveland took Thomas 3ʳᵈ overall, Thomas found out through a cell phone call while he was out on the middle of a lake.

4. Cleveland has chosen three Alabama Crimson Tide players in the top 10 of the NFL Draft, more than any other school. The team selected running back Trent Richardson 3ʳᵈ overall in 2012, defensive back Antonio Langham 9ᵗʰ overall in 1994, and offensive tackle Jedrick Wills Jr. 10ᵗʰ overall in 2020.

5. The Browns have drafted two players from the University of Ohio Bobcats: linebacker Dick Grecni in 1960 and end Ted Stute in 1962. Neither local selection worked out, as

Grecni played just 12 games in the NFL, and Stute did not play at all.

6. Cleveland has drafted 10 players who have played just a single game in the NFL. Only two of them (defensive backs Trey Caldwell and Ricky Stevenson) made that appearance with the Browns, and the rest had their lone moment to shine after catching on with other franchises.

7. Of the draft spots in the top 10 in the NFL Draft, Cleveland has selected at 3rd overall more than any other, choosing six players in that position. Best among them was probably offensive tackle Joe Thomas, who spent over a decade with the Browns and will one day be a strong candidate for the Hall of Fame.

8. The smallest draft classes ever selected by the Browns in the NFL Draft came in 2008 and 2013; they took just five players each of those years.

9. The Cleveland Browns were the team featured prominently in the 2014 movie *Draft Day*. In the movie, Oscar-winning actor Kevin Costner portrays the (fictional) general manager of the Browns, Sonny Weaver, as the team approaches the NFL Draft. The movie offers a look into the process behind drafting college prospects, and Weaver faces a typical dilemma that a real GM would have to deal with as well: go with the consensus or stick to his gut.

10. The latest pick the Browns have made in the NFL Draft was wide receiver Tom Fleming from Dartmouth

University, whom the team chose 464th overall in 1976. Fleming never made it to the NFL. Defensive back Ben Davis, the team's 439th overall pick from Defiance University in 1967, was the latest pick they've made who actually played for the team, as he spent seven seasons with Cleveland.

CHAPTER 11:

COACHES, GMS, & OWNERS

QUIZ TIME!

1. Who served as the Browns' first general manager?

   a. Harold Sauerbrei

   b. Dwight Clark

   c. Ernie Accorsi

   d. Paul Brown

2. Cleveland general manager Butch Davis once proposed a deal with the New England Patriots that would have sent 1st overall pick, quarterback Tim Couch, to Massachusetts in exchange for a young and then little-known Tom Brady.

   a. True

   b. False

3. The Browns' first head coach, Paul Brown, lasted for how long in that position with the franchise?

   a. 8 games

   b. 32 games

c. 150 games

d. 214 games

4. The Browns' most recent coach, Kevin Stefanski, rose through the coaching ranks by holding seven different coaching positions with which other NFL franchise before Cleveland hired him as head man?

a. Minnesota Vikings

b. New York Giants

c. New England Patriots

d. New Orleans Saints

5. Who has owned the Cleveland Browns for the longest amount of time?

a. Paul Brown

b. Arthur McBride

c. Art Modell

d. Jimmy Haslam III

6. Of all the Cleveland bench bosses who have coached over 50 NFL games with the team, which one had the lowest winning percentage at only .375?

a. Romeo Crennel

b. Butch Davis

c. Hugh Jackson

d. Bill Belichick

7. Cleveland is the only NFL franchise to have a player rise from competing on the field for the team to owning the team.

a. True

b. False

8. Which coach led the Browns to their first NFL Championship?

a. Blanton Collier

b. Marty Schottenheimer

c. Paul Brown

d. Bill Belichick

9. Which Cleveland general manager once took the field as a player on the team before getting the chance to guide it from the front office?

a. Dwight Clark

b. Bernie Kosar

c. John Dorsey

d. Ozzie Newsome

10. Who is the Cleveland leader in coaching wins?

a. Sam Rutigliano

b. Marty Schottenheimer

c. Forrest Gregg

d. Paul Brown

11. The shortest ownership term for a Cleveland Browns owner is held by Al Lerner. For how long did he own the team before passing away due to brain cancer?

a. 1 year

b. 3 years

c. 5 years

d. 8 years

12. Coach Paul Brown's 1948 AAFC season is the Browns' benchmark in terms of winning percentage, as he led the team to a perfect 14-0 record in the regular season.

    a. True
    b. False

13. How many of the official (not interim) Browns head coaches have spent their entire NFL coaching career with Cleveland?

    a. 2
    b. 5
    c. 8
    d. 11

14. Which Browns general manager has led the franchise to the most playoff appearances?

    a. Harold Sauerbrei
    b. John Dorsey
    c. Paul Brown
    d. Ernie Accorsi

15. Out of 17 seasons coaching the Browns, how many times did coach Paul Brown finish above .500?

    a. 16
    b. 12
    c. 8
    d. 17

16. Over one decade, the Browns employed four coaches who had all started for Cleveland during their playing careers.

a. True

b. False

17. How did Al Lerner become the majority owner of the Browns in 1999?

    a. He purchased the team when the previous owners wished to sell.

    b. He inherited the team when his father passed away.

    c. He forced a takeover of the corporation that had previously owned the team.

    d. He won an open auction competition with a $530 million bid.

18. How many official (not interim) head coaches have roamed the sidelines for the Browns in their history?

    a. 8

    b. 11

    c. 18

    d. 26

19. Which two Browns coaches are the only ones to have won the Associated Press Award as the league's top coach while with Cleveland?

    a. Forrest Gregg and Kevin Stefanski

    b. Paul Brown and Marty Schottenheimer

    c. Bill Belichick and Romeo Crennel

    d. Blanton Collier and Gregg Williams

20. Browns owner Al Lerner once proposed trading franchises with New York Yankees owner George Steinbrenner as part of a business deal.

    a. True
    b. False

QUIZ ANSWERS

1. D – Paul Brown

2. B – False

3. D – 214 games

4. A – Minnesota Vikings

5. C – Art Modell

6. A – Romeo Crennel

7. B – False

8. C – Paul Brown

9. D – Ozzie Newsome

10. D – Paul Brown

11. B – 3 years

12. A – True

13. D – 11

14. C – Paul Brown

15. A – 16

16. B – False

17. D – He won an open auction competition with a $530 million bid.

18. C – 18

19. A – Forrest Gregg and Kevin Stefanski

20. B – False

DID YOU KNOW?

1. Four times in team history, the Browns fired a coach midway through a season. Hugh Jackson was given the shortest runway and was let go after just eight games in the 2018 season. In addition, head coach Butch Davis resigned during the 2004 season after the team had struggled through its first eleven games.

2. Three men have served as both coach and general manager of the Browns. Butch Davis was the most recent, as he held both positions from 2002 to 2004; not long after, Bill Belichick did the same from 1992 to 1995.

3. Cleveland namesake Paul Brown was a major innovator in the world of football. Among the many ideas introduced by Brown were: watching game film to prepare for upcoming games, creating the facemask attached to helmets, the development of the practice squad, and racial integration (Cleveland broke the color barrier in professional football).

4. The Browns' original general manager, Paul Brown, did an incredible job. Brown lasted in the position from 1946 through 1962, and also served as the team's head coach during that entire tenure. Cleveland won seven titles during this tenure.

5. The first two Browns head coaches, Paul Brown and Blanton Collier, who served the team for a combined 24

years in the position, actually met in the Navy during World War II. Brown was impressed with Collier and hired him to be an assistant coach after the war ended.

6. Head coach Sam Rutigliano leads the Cleveland Browns with the most regular-season losses (50). When playoff games are factored in as well, Paul Brown takes over the lead with 53 total losses.

7. In recent times, the Browns have cycled through general managers very quickly. Since 2008, the team has employed eight men in the position, with an average tenure of less than two years apiece.

8. Before becoming arguably the greatest head coach in NFL history with the New England Patriots, Bill Belichick spent five seasons as the Browns' sideline boss. Though Belichick won a playoff game with Cleveland, his teams had losing seasons in four of his five years with the franchise.

9. Franchise legend and Pro Football Hall-of-Famer Paul Brown was a major figure across the NFL. Brown founded not only the Cleveland Browns but also the Cincinnati Bengals. Cincinnati still plays in Paul Brown Stadium.

10. Never in league history has a Cleveland general manager been awarded *The Sporting News* NFL Executive of the Year Award. To be fair, the award was discontinued during the Browns' most successful years and did not return to circulation until 1972.

CHAPTER 12:

ODDS & ENDS

QUIZ TIME!

1. Who has won the most league MVP trophies, awarded by the Associated Press, while playing for Cleveland?

    a. Running back Jim Brown

    b. Quarterback Brian Sipe

    c. Quarterback Otto Graham

    d. Tackle/placekicker Lou Groza

2. The first Brown to win any major award given out by the NFL was franchise tight end Ozzie Newsome.

    a. True

    b. False

3. During which season did the Browns win their first Vince Lombardi Trophy as Super Bowl champions?

    a. 1953

    b. 1966

    c. 1971

    d. The Browns have never won a Super Bowl.

4. In 2019, the NFL announced its All-Time Team, recognizing the 100 greatest players from the first 100 years of NFL history. How many of these players suited up for the Browns?

    a. 3 on offense, 3 on defense, and 1 on special teams
    b. 2 on offense, 5 on defense, and 2 on special teams
    c. 4 on offense, 0 on defense, and 0 on special teams
    d. 1 on offense, 2 on defense, and 1 on special teams

5. How many Cleveland Browns have won a recognized version of the Comeback Player of the Year Award (including the Associated Press, Pro Football Writers Association, Sporting News, or United Press International awards)?

    a. 0
    b. 2
    c. 3
    d. 5

6. What is Jim Donovan's connection to the Cleveland Browns?

    a. An architect who designed and built FirstEnergy Stadium for the Browns
    b. A beloved groundskeeper who has worked for the Browns since 1983
    c. A player agent who represented quarterback Baker Mayfield, cornerback Joe Haden, and several others
    d. A longtime radio announcer for the Browns on their home station

7. The Cleveland Browns have the most wins of any franchise in NFL history.

    a. True
    b. False

8. The Browns have employed multiple quarterbacks who won the Heisman Trophy while playing in college. Which of the following is NOT among them?

    a. Vinny Testaverde
    b. Bernie Kosar
    c. Johnny Manziel
    d. Baker Mayfield

9. How many Browns players have won the NFL's Defensive Player of the Year Award?

    a. 1: linebacker Clay Matthews Jr.
    b. 2: linebacker Clay Matthews Jr. and defensive end Myles Garrett
    c. 4: linebacker Clay Matthews Jr, defensive end Myles Garrett, middle guard Bill Willis, and cornerback Hanford Dixon
    d. No Cleveland Browns player has ever won this award.

10. Only one player has played an entire career of at least 20 years for the Browns without ever starting a game for another NFL franchise. Which loyal athlete played only for Cleveland for that long?

    a. Running back Jim Brown
    b. Quarterback Otto Graham

c. Offensive tackle Lou Groza

d. Linebacker Clay Matthews Jr.

11. Defensive tackle Dick Modzelewski was a key member of the 1964 championship team in Cleveland and also won a second NFL Championship with which other franchise?

a. Washington Redskins

b. Pittsburgh Steelers

c. Miami Dolphins

d. New York Giants

12. Cleveland is the first NFL team to win the Super Bowl after losing the previous year.

a. True

b. False

13. Although his average yards per punt was 43.1, Browns punter Horace Gillom set the Cleveland record for longest punt in franchise history by dropping one that traveled how far?

a. 70 yards

b. 76 yards

c. 80 yards

d. 91 yards

14. Of the Browns in the Football Hall of Fame, seven of them began to play with Cleveland during the Browns' inaugural 1946 season in the AAFC. Which of the following position groups is NOT represented among those original inductees?

a. Defensive backs

b. Wide receivers

c. Quarterbacks

d. Offensive line

15. Cleveland kicker Phil Dawson holds the franchise record for the most consecutive field goals made. How many kicks in a row did he convert during this streak?

    a. 11

    b. 18

    c. 29

    d. 36

16. Kicker Lou Groza, who played 21 years for the Browns, *missed* more field goals during his career than any other Cleveland player has even *attempted*.

    a. True

    b. False

17. Which Browns kicker (with at least 50 kicks attempted) holds the team's highest field goal percentage, at 84% made?

    a. Lou Groza

    b. Matt Bahr

    c. Matt Stover

    d. Phil Dawson

18. Which team has defeated the Browns 75 times, more often than any other in the team's history?

    a. Pittsburgh Steelers

    b. Denver Broncos

c. Cincinnati Bengals

d. Tennessee Titans

19. Which current NFL franchise have the Browns played less often than any other team, squaring off against each other just six times?

a. Carolina Panthers

b. Buffalo Bills

c. Tampa Bay Buccaneers

d. Kansas City Chiefs

20. The Browns won four NFL Championships before the Super Bowl era began, and all four times they were victorious in a home game at Cleveland Stadium.

a. True

b. False

QUIZ ANSWERS

1. A – Running back Jim Brown

2. B – False

3. D – The Browns have never won a Super Bowl.

4. C – 4 on offense, 0 on defense, and 0 on special teams

5. A – 0

6. D – A longtime radio announcer for the Browns on their home station

7. B – False

8. B – Bernie Kosar

9. D – No Cleveland Browns player has ever won this award.

10. C – Offensive tackle Lou Groza

11. D – New York Giants

12. B – False

13. C – 80 yards

14. A – Defensive backs

15. C – 29

16. B – False

17. D – Phil Dawson

18. A – Pittsburgh Steelers

19. A – Carolina Panthers

20. B – False

DID YOU KNOW?

1. No Cleveland player has won the NFL's Walter Payton Man of the Year Award. The team's most recent nominee was defensive end Myles Garett in 2020.

2. The largest lead that Cleveland has ever blown is a 23-point advantage that the Browns held over the Philadelphia Eagles on November 10, 1991. A hot start leading to a 23-0 score early in the second quarter was methodically erased, resulting in an Eagles win with the final score of 32-30.

3. Browns icon Jim Brown sits just outside the top 10 on the list of the NFL's career rushing yards leaders. Brown ranks 11th all-time with 12,312 yards on the ground. He is 33 yards ahead of St. Louis Rams star Marshall Faulk and 427 yards behind Tony Dorsett of the Dallas Cowboys.

4. The biggest comeback in Cleveland history came on October 15, 2014. Down by 25 points to the Tennessee Titans, the Browns stormed back to secure a thrilling 29-28 victory behind a big day from quarterback Brian Hoyer and two touchdowns from wide receiver Travis Benjamin.

5. The Browns' value is estimated at $2.35 billion by *Forbes* magazine, which ranks them as the 26th most valuable NFL team, right between the Jacksonville Jaguars and Arizona Cardinals.

6. In 2020, Cleveland's live mascot, a 145-pound dog named "Swagger," passed away from cancer at the age of six. The beloved bull mastiff was at the front of the pack as the team emerged from the stadium tunnel before home games, a duty that will now be taken over by Swagger's son, "SJ."

7. Cleveland has a winning record against 13 other current NFL teams. The Browns have got the better of the Bills, Falcons, Washington Football Team, Saints, Cardinals, Eagles, 49ers, Buccaneers, Bears, Giants, Cowboys, Titans, and Jets.

8. The Browns have played more games against the Pittsburgh Steelers than any other team in the NFL, and it isn't close. The two clubs have faced off 136 times, with only one other club (the Cincinnati Bengals) within even 40 games of that mark. Cleveland is 60-75-1 in that series, good for a .445 winning percentage.

9. In 2001, the Browns nearly played a game against the Jacksonville Jaguars that was shorter than every other NFL game. After a disputed call was reversed by the referees, Browns fans littered the playing field with beer bottles and garbage cans, causing officials to call the game with 48 seconds left on the clock. Everyone left the field but did eventually return for two kneel-downs after the NFL called and insisted that the game be finished.

10. Two Browns legends have received honorary statues outside of FirstEnergy Stadium. Running back Jim Brown's

statue was built in 2016, and quarterback Otto Graham's was completed in 2019.

CONCLUSION

There you have it; an amazing collection of Browns trivia, information, and statistics at your fingertips! Regardless of how you fared on the quizzes, we hope that you found this book entertaining, enlightening, and educational.

Ideally, you knew many of these details but also learned a good deal more about the history of the Cleveland Browns, their players, coaches, management, and some of the quirky stories surrounding the team. If you got a little peek into the colorful details that make being a fan so much more enjoyable, then mission accomplished!

The good news is that the trivia doesn't have to stop there! Spread the word. Challenge your fellow Browns fans to see if they can do any better. Share some of the stories with the next generation to help them become Cleveland supporters too.

If you are a big enough Browns fan, consider creating your own quiz with some of the details you know that weren't presented here and then test your friends to see if they can match your knowledge.

The Cleveland Browns are a storied franchise. They have a long history with multiple periods of success and a few that were less than successful. They've had glorious superstars, iconic moments, hilarious tales…but most of all, they have wonderful, passionate fans. Thank you for being one of them.

Made in the USA
Middletown, DE
20 December 2021

56754034R00080